For
Bunny

LADYBIRD IQ TESTS Vol I

Sam Rabbit
(Bunny)

First Published 1993
by Brownsword Books
28 Gay Street · Bath
England · BA1 2PD

Printed and bound
in Great Britain

ISBN 1 873615 96 5

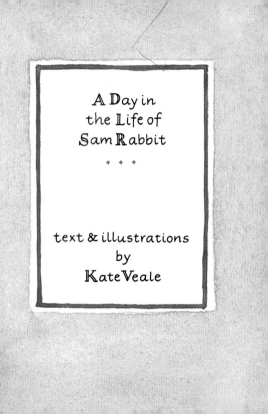

A Day in
the Life of
Sam Rabbit

◆ ◆ ◆

text & illustrations
by
Kate Veale

" I don't have a set daily routine but I like to be tidy and to keep things in order. I make a lot of lists; shopping lists, lists of jobs for the day, lists of things to do and football scores."

LIST OF
LISTS
• SHOPPING
LIST
• DON'T FORGET
LIST
• THINGS TO DO
IN WINTER
LIST
• FOOTBALL

"I keep lists of the football scores so that I can check the football lottery. If you guess the scores correctly you can win prizes. I won an address book once which was really useful because mouse and I have lots of cousins."

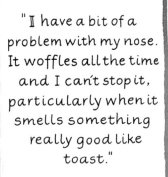

" I have a bit of a problem with my nose. It woffles all the time and I can't stop it, particularly when it smells something really good like toast."

"I've had to get used to it though and the others, Mouse, Ed and Badger say that they like my nose anyway because it can smell food from a long way off."

We like
your
nose!

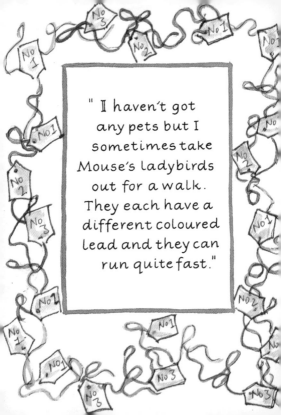

" I haven't got any pets but I sometimes take Mouse's ladybirds out for a walk. They each have a different coloured lead and they can run quite fast."

" Their favourite
walk is to the post box.
I think it must be
because it's red
and black and
reminds them of
a large ladybird."

"Ladybirds can fly too,
but these prefer
running and walking.
I tried to get them to
fly once by saying the
old rhyme:
Ladybird, ladybird
fly away home,
your house is on fire
and your children
are gone!"

"But they just said that they preferred living in Mouse's house and that they don't have any children anyway. You can't trick these ladybirds!"

LADYBIRD IQ TESTS VOL. I

" I like going for walks,
particularly in the
autumn when the
leaves have fallen
ankle deep on the
ground and you can
wade through them
and make a huge
crunching noise."

" In the winter I go ski-ing, which is like going for a walk only faster. That reminds me, I must start my winter list of 'Things to Do' with 'remember to wax skis'. So I'd better go."

Kate Veale starts her day at around 6.30 a.m., when the noise from the street below wakes her. She lives in the old quarter of Innsbruck in the Tirol, working most days from around 9 a.m. She likes lots of things (particularly chocolate!) and loves ski-ing, the mountains, wildlife, and visiting different countries.